Saint George

A Christmas Mummers' Play

Saint George

A Christmas Mummers' Play

Katherine Miller

Illustrated by Wallace Tripp

HOUGHTON MIFFLIN COMPANY BOSTON 1967

For Donn
and his Mummers' band

Katherine Miller has also written

Five Plays from Shakespeare

Preface

For longer than anyone knows, the merrymaking associated with the celebration of holidays and festivals of old England has included simple plays along with (or incorporated in) the singing and dancing and feasting. Handed down by memory from one year to the next, generation after generation, these folk plays underwent many metamorphoses. By the time any effort was made to record them, around the turn of the last century, some were almost unintelligible, and of many only fragments were remembered. Most of those we have record of fall into two categories, Saint George Christmas plays, and Robin Hood May Day plays. Of these, by far the greatest number are the Christmas plays. Collected in widely separated areas, they show amazing similarities: similar characters, similar events, sometimes even similar speeches.

Much discussion has been generated as to the origins and meanings of the plays and their strange assortment of characters. It seems not improbable that Saint George is a distant descendant of the hero of a lost medieval miracle play for there were a number based on the lives of saints. Being a colorful character, Saint George caught the fancy of the people and so achieved true immortality. But is the Doctor, really descended from some ancient pagan priest celebrating the yearly death and resurrection of an ancient pagan nature god? Who knows? It is fun to speculate, and folklorists have done a deal of it. But does it matter greatly? Whatever the origins, and whatever the meanings, the plays have given delight to generations, are a part of the heritage of folkways and customs belonging to everyone whose native tongue is English.

Here, therefore, patched together from many old plays and dances, its sense pieced out here and there for modern audiences, and revived with a dash of hokum-pokum, is

Saint George

A Christmas Mummers' Play

Gay with holly and mistletoe, and fragrant with wood smoke from the fire blazing in the great fireplace, the room is filled to bursting with noise and bustle and laughter of children and grown-ups — brothers, sisters, mothers, fathers, cousins, grandparents, uncles, aunts, all gathered together. It is Christmas time.

There comes a knock on an outer door, a gust of cold air as the door is opened, a "Please, ma'am, is it all right if we come in now?" in the hall, and the delighted cry spreads from child to child like ripples in a pool: "The mummers! the mummers! the mummers!" Instantly the chatter dies, all eyes turn to the doorway and there they are, crowded together in the opening, face

behind face, face above face, their masks and headdresses picked out in the light falling on them from candles and roaring fire: the mummers!

"Clear a place for the mummers!" someone shouts.

Children and grown-ups scurry to find seats on stools and benches and floor, or push back to stand against the wall, making room for the mummers and their play. Farm boys they are, these mummers, as their rough trousers and boots testify — for although they are gaily and fantastically costumed from the waist up, they seem to think fancy dress unnecessary for their lower extremities. In crowded rooms few can see their legs in any event, so why subject cherished finery to the risk of being splashed by the slush and mire of muddy roads as they trudge about the dark countryside?

Just such a scene as this could be found on almost any night of the Christmas season in any of scores of villages and hamlets all over England as recently as fifty years ago, or perhaps as long ago as the days of the crusaders. Just how long ago, no one can say. For centuries, though, as surely as Christmas came to England, so surely came the mummers, crowding into houses and halls of the great and the not-great, bringing their bit of nonsense to add to the general merriment of Christmas time.

What a weird assortment the characters are, in these mummers' plays! First of all there is a Presenter. He comes in many guises, though always he is something of a clown, and with many

names: Tom Fool, Big Head, Little Johnny Jack, Johnny Finny, or Old Hind Before (who comes in backward). Sometimes the Presenter is a woman, and frequently he is Father Christmas himself. It is the Presenter's job to call for attention and introduce — or rather to present, for they need no introduction — the familiar characters.

Into the center of the ring of expectant children in this particular firelit room bounces Little Johnny Jack! His coat is a patchwork of many colors, and he waves a balloon on a stick that jingles with sleigh bells.

LITTLE JOHNNY JACK
    Here come I — little Johnny Jack,
    With a pack of merry boys at my back.
    We are a Christmas Mummers' band,
    Sons of the soil of old Eng-land.
    Some can't dance and some can't sing,
    But we hope your favor we shall win.
    Come in, Father Christmas! Time to begin.

Into the charmed circle now comes a red-cheeked Father Christmas, wearing a crown of holly on his white head and carrying a big bag slung over his back.

FATHER CHRISTMAS
    Ho, ho, ho, ho!
    Welcome or welcome not, here I come —
    Old Father Christmas, to start the fun.
    Christmas comes but once a year
    And when it comes it brings good cheer:
    Roast beef, plum pudding, and mince pie!
    Who likes that any better than I?

HOBBY HORSE
> (*Whinnies*) Me - ee - ee - ee!

LITTLE JOHNNY JACK
> Come in, come in, Hobby Horse!

But the Hobby Horse is already very much in. Around the circle of children he prances. They pat his nose and pull his tail, squealing with delight when he bends his head down to nuzzle at a neck. This Hobby Horse has only two legs, as it happens, and those are trousered and end in feet shod with heavy boots, but no one seems to mind. In fact, all of him that might properly be called horse is his tail of black yarn and his head — a wooden hobbyhorse head from which falls a great enveloping skirt-like cloth. But to the children he is all horse, and they love his prancing and whinnying. Finally Johnny Jack seizes his reins to calm him down and get on with the play.

LITTLE JOHNNY JACK
  Whoa, boy, whoa!
FATHER CHRISTMAS
  Stir up the fire, folks, strike a light,
  And see our merry boys act tonight.
  We're going to show you Saint George's play.
  Come in, Mother Dolly, and clear the way!
And Mother Dolly capers in with her broom, a kerchief on her head and a voluminous skirt awkwardly covering her lanky boy legs.
MOTHER DOLLY
  In come I, old Mother Dolly,
  Come for Christmas fun and folly.

Before we begin, I have to make room —
I'll sweep you away with my little broom.
Room, make room! Give us room to rhyme,
And we'll show you a play for Christmas time!

Vigorously she sweeps at toes and knees of the littlest ones sitting cross-legged on the floor, and back they push into any spare nooks and crannies between the knees and feet behind them.

LITTLE JOHNNY JACK
In this room there shall be shown
The most dreadfullest battles that ever were known.
A dragon you shall see —
A wild worm for to flee!
And England's brave Saint George shall fight
Against the terrible Turkish Knight.
Come in, Saint George! Come in, Turkish Knight!

In strides the smiling hero of the evening, followed by the terrible Turk. Saint George is clad in pure white, with a great red cross on his noble breast, but the smock of his dread antago-

nist-to-be is as black as his heathen heart. The two knights bow and take their places — at opposite ends of the lengthening line of characters.

    LITTLE JOHNNY JACK

        Come in, Fiery Dragon, and boldly begin!

    Here, at last, is the children's favorite! He shuffles in, rumbling and roaring, snuffling and snorting. His long saw-toothed jaw hangs a bit askew, and jagged bits of red-silk flame

flutter from his nostrils. Back and forth he paces, the excited
children shrieking and ducking when he approaches them.

    FIERY DRAGON

        In come I, the Dragon bold,
        And Slasher is my name.
        If your blood runs hot, I'll make it cold,
        A-breathing fire and flame!
        Meat, meat, meat for to eat!
        I am the Dragon — here are my jaws.
        I am the Dragon — here are my claws.
        Meat, meat, meat for to eat!

At this tense moment Mother Dolly steps forward. She removes the kerchief from her head, ties it around her hips, and behold! — an exotic beauty in a wig of long straight black hair!

MOTHER DOLLY

    Now I'll be the King of Egypt's daughter,
    Victim of the Dragon's slaughter.

FIERY DRAGON

    Meat, meat, meat for to eat!
    I am the Dragon — here are my jaws.
    I am the Dragon — here are my claws.
    Meat, meat, meat for to eat!

Suddenly he turns and seizes in his terrible claws the King of Egypt's beautiful daughter!

MOTHER DOLLY
>   Oh, save me, save me, Saint George, save me!

And Saint George steps forward to rush to her rescue. — Or does he? No! First he stops to boast of his bravery. Back and forth he struts, uttering his ringing phrases, while the Dragon, who could have gobbled down his victim in half the time, waits patiently for Saint George to have his say.

SAINT GEORGE
>   Here come I, Saint George, to the rescue bravely!
>   I'll fight the Dragon — I'm not shy.
>   I'll clip his wings, he shall not fly.
>   I'll cut him down — or else I die!

FIERY DRAGON

    Who is it seeks the Dragon's blood,
    And calls so angry and so loud?

SAINT GEORGE

    I'm he who seeks the Dragon's blood,
    And calls so angry and so loud!

FIERY DRAGON

    I'll seize you with my steely claws —
    With my long teeth and scurvy jaws!

SAINT GEORGE

    And I will kill you till you're dead.
    With one blow I'll lop off your head!

FIERY DRAGON

    My head is made of iron,
    My body is made of steel,

My arms and legs are beaten brass,
No man can make me feel!

SAINT GEORGE

Well, mind your head, and guard my blows —
And also watch that great long nose!

He thumps the Dragon smartly on the nose with his wooden sword, and with that the fight is on. Bravely Saint George slashes at Slasher, who roars a mighty roar and claws viciously at his mortal enemy, his prey now entirely forgotten. It is a lovely battle! Finally, though, the antagonists fall, both of them — dead? the children wonder?

MOTHER DOLLY

Get up, Saint George, old England's Knight,
Thou hast killed the Dragon and finished the fight!

Up he gets! Saint George is alive! He wasn't dead, after all. Proudly he waves his victorious sword as he stands with his foot on his fallen foe.

SAINT GEORGE
> I am Saint George, old England's pride,
> A man of courage bold!
> With sword and buckler by my side,
> I won a crown of gold!
> I fought the Fiery Dragon and drove
>   him to the slaughter,
> And by these deeds I saved the King
>   of Egypt's daughter!

He gestures toward the lady. She smiles and curtsies to one and all; then, her part played, she covers her black hair with her kerchief and is once more old Mother Dolly. As for the Dragon — it is up to Little Johnny Jack and Father Christmas to dispose of him, and out into the entrance hall they drag his ugly carcass.

LITTLE JOHNNY JACK
> Come, one behind and one before,
> We'll drag this Dragon out the door.

FATHER CHRISTMAS
> Heave ho! Out you go!

Saint George has paused in his declaiming long enough for the stage to be cleared. He may be bold enough to fight with the Dragon for the King of Egypt's daughter, but he is not fool enough to compete with him for the attention of the audience!

SAINT GEORGE
> I fear no Spanish, French, nor Turk.
> There's no man that can do me hurt.
> Show me a man that against me dare stand;
> I'll cut him down with my courageous hand!

TURKISH KNIGHT
> Here am I, the Turkish Knight,
> Come from Turkish land to fight.

Far have I come, from over the seas;
I can kill ten thousand!

SAINT GEORGE

(*Aside*) If they be fleas!

TURKISH KNIGHT

Where is the man that dares me to stand?
Who would cut me down with his audacious hand?
A battle, a battle with him will I try,
To see who on the ground shall lie!

SAINT GEORGE

Thou speakest very brash and bold
To such a man as I.
I'll cut thy doublet full of holes
And make thy buttons fly.
So stand off, black and Turkish dog!
Let nothing more be said.
For if I wield my bloody sword,
I'm sure to break your head!

TURKISH KNIGHT

I'll hack you and hew you into pieces small as flies
And send you to the cookshop to make mince pies:
Mince pies hot,
Mince pies cold,
I'll send you to the devil 'fore you're nine days old!

SAINT GEORGE

Here is my sword. Now let us battle,
And I will make your bones to rattle!

But the Turkish Knight points with scorn at Saint George's
sword.

TURKISH KNIGHT

A fool, a fool — that man's a fool
Who wears a wooden sword!

SAINT GEORGE

A wooden sword? Thou dirty dog,
I'll make thee eat that word!

Thereupon the two knights set to with a great clattering clash of wooden swords (for the Turk's sword is wooden too, of course). Quickly George knocks the sword from the Turkish Knight's hand, forces him to his knees, and stands over him. He has him at his mercy.

TURKISH KNIGHT

    Pardon me! Oh, pardon I crave,

    And I will be thy Turkish slave!

SAINT GEORGE

    I never will pardon a Turkish Knight;

    Therefore, take up thy sword and fight.

The watching children cheer their valiant Saint George as he kicks the cowardly Turk's sword to him, and they fight again. But this time — alas, alas — this time Saint George is the one to fall.

SAINT GEORGE

    My blood is spilled by this Turkish knight.

    I die for England and the right!

And with a dramatic groan Saint George dies.

FATHER CHRISTMAS

    Oh, cruel Knight, what hast thou done?

    Thou hast killed my only son!

TURKISH KNIGHT

    (Shrugs.) But it was he who challenged me!

MOTHER DOLLY

 Oh, Doctor, Doctor, where be thee?

 Saint George is wounded through the knee.

 Doctor, Doctor, play thy part.

 Saint George is wounded through the heart.

FATHER CHRISTMAS

 Is there a doctor to be found,

 To cure this deep and deadly wound?

HOBBY HORSE

 Me — ee — ee! — Whoa, boy, whoa!

It is the horse who speaks! Off comes his head (and the attached drapery), and there is the Doctor, dressed in high collar, ascot, and long black tailcoat and spectacles. His hip pocket bulges with a bottle; a huge wooden spoon is in his belt.

DOCTOR

Yes, here's a Doctor to be found,
To cure his deep and deadly wound.

MOTHER DOLLY

What, you a Doctor?

DOCTOR

Yes, me a Doctor.

MOTHER DOLLY

Then tell me, Doctor, what's your fee?

DOCTOR

Full fifty pounds I'll have of thee.

MOTHER DOLLY

Full fifty pounds?

DOCTOR

Well, take off five,
If I don't save this man alive.

FATHER CHRISTMAS

What can you do, and what can you cure?

DOCTOR

All sorts of diseases: wheezes, and sneezes,
And anything else that my physic pleases —
The itch, the stitch, the palsy, the gout,
Pains in the belly and pains all about.
And if he's got the devil in him,
I can fetch it out!

FATHER CHRISTMAS

How came you to be a Doctor?

DOCTOR

By my travels.

FATHER CHRISTMAS

Where have you traveled?

DOCTOR

Through Italy, Sicily, France, and Spain,
Nine times round the world and back again.

FATHER CHRISTMAS

But tell me, Doctor, have you come
All that way since supper?

DOCTOR
>Yes, I have, upon my pony —
>Knock-kneed bobtailed, without e'er a crupper.
>Here, hold him, Jack.

Without warning he suddenly thrusts the Hobby Horse at a startled Johnny Jack, who takes it somewhat reluctantly, and examines it warily.

LITTLE JOHNNY JACK
 Will he bite?
DOCTOR
 No.
LITTLE JOHNNY JACK
 Take two to hold him?
DOCTOR
 No.

LITTLE JOHNNY JACK

Hold him yourself, then!

And back comes the Horse to the Doctor.

DOCTOR

What's that, you saucy young rascal?

Swinging the Hobby Horse like a club, the Doctor chases
Jack around the room.

LITTLE JOHNNY JACK
    Oh, I hold him, sir! Got fast hold of his tail, sir!
DOCTOR
    Give him a good stiff feed of water, and a drink of hay.
LITTLE JOHNNY JACK
    Do it yourself, sir.
Again he thrusts the Horse at the Doctor, and again the
Doctor chases him with it.
DOCTOR
    What's that, you saucy young rascal?
LITTLE JOHNNY JACK
    Oh, I do it, sir!
So Jack deposits the Hobby Horse with the Dragon in the
hallway.

DOCTOR

(To Mother Dolly) This the dead man? Here, hold my bottle while I feel his pulse.

The Doctor takes a bottle from his pocket, hands it to Mother Dolly, and kneels beside his patient. He pats George on his stomach, and leans down to put his ear against his stomach.

MOTHER DOLLY

Is that where a man's pulse lies?

Instead of replying the Doctor taps George's head with his wooden spoon, and a "clunk, clunk, clunk" sounds eerily from the

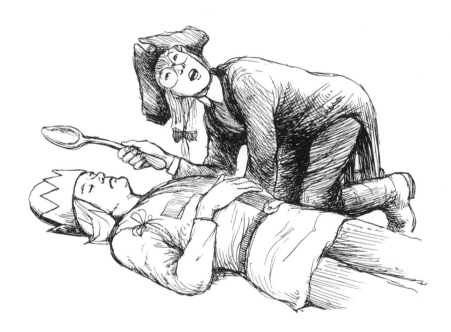

hall. Then he opens George's mouth to peer in; the screak of a rusty hinge comes from the hall.

DOCTOR

Tsk, tsk, tsk. This man is terrible sick. He's got
a tooth in his head! And besides that, he's dead!

MOTHER DOLLY

Oh, Doctor, can you cure him?

DOCTOR

>That I can! Why, if he's seven years wed, eight years dead, nine years laid in his grave, I can cure him! Fetch me my lance, Jack.

LITTLE JOHNNY JACK

>Fetch it yourself, sir!

DOCTOR

>What's that, you saucy young rascal?

Once more he threatens to beat Jack, this time with his wooden spoon.

LITTLE JOHNNY JACK

>Oh, I'm going as fast as I can, sir! There it is, sir.

He has fetched a saw from Father Christmas's bag, and he throws it to the floor beside the Doctor.

DOCTOR

>What did you throw it down there for?

LITTLE JOHNNY JACK

    Ah, for thee to pick it up again, sir.

DOCTOR

    What's that, you saucy young rascal?

Again he threatens Jack. The children seem never to get too much of this kind of business, so over and over it repeats itself to their never-ending delight.

LITTLE JOHNNY JACK

Ah, for me to pick it up again, sir.

He picks up the saw and, with a deep bow, hands it to the Doctor who saws a moment at Saint George's neck; then discards the instrument in disgust.

DOCTOR

Fetch me my pincers, Jack.

LITTLE JOHNNY JACK

Fetch them yourself, sir!

DOCTOR

What's that, you saucy young rascal?

LITTLE JOHNNY JACK

Oh, I fetch them, sir! There they are, sir.

DOCTOR

What did you throw them down there for?

LITTLE JOHNNY JACK

Ah, for thee to pick them up again, sir.

DOCTOR

What's that, you saucy young rascal?

LITTLE JOHNNY JACK

Oh, for me to pick them up again, sir!

With the pincers the Doctor pulls at Saint George's tooth to no avail.

DOCTOR

Fetch me one of the strongest hosses you've got in your team.

LITTLE JOHNNY JACK

Fetch him yourself, sir!

DOCTOR

What's that, you saucy young rascal?

LITTLE JOHNNY JACK

Oh, I'll fetch him, sir! Whoa, whoa, whoa!
There he is, sir.

What is this horse the rascal has brought? It is none other than old Father Christmas, led by the beard for a bridle.

DOCTOR

    You call that the strongest hoss you've got in the
    team?

LITTLE JOHNNY JACK

    That's him, sir.

DOCTOR

    Hold him tight then, Jack.

LITTLE JOHNNY JACK

    Hold him yourself, sir!

With a push he sends Father Christmas stumbling against
the Doctor.

DOCTOR

    What's that, you saucy young rascal?

Poor old Father Christmas! Back he stumbles toward Jack.

LITTLE JOHNNY JACK

    Oh, I've got him, sir, fast by the tail!

The now obedient Jack gets behind Father Christmas and
throws both arms around his waist.

DOCTOR
Now catch hold of me and pull, boys.
The Doctor has his pincers set firmly in Saint George's
gaping mouth. Father Christmas takes hold of the Doctor's waist,

and the other mummers line up behind Jack as if for a tug of war.
DOCTOR
    A long pull, a short pull, pull all together, boys!
With a one, a two, and a three, they give a mighty heave.

Back they stagger, down they fall, all in a pile — and woe to the onlooker who wasn't quick enough to scramble out of their way.

    LITTLE JOHNNY JACK

        Be he out, sir?

    DOCTOR

        No! — Now again, boys, together, boys catch hold of
        me and pull!

Once more they pull; once more they fall.

    LITTLE JOHNNY JACK

        Be he out yet, sir?

    DOCTOR

        Yes! We've got him this time, Jack!

Triumphantly he raises his pincers high to show his prize:
a tooth — a huge, an enormous, a gigantic tooth!

DOCTOR

> And more like a helephant's tooth than a Christian's:
> As long as a ten-penny nail, and got roots like a poplar
> tree! — Ladies and gentlemen all, this large wolf's
> tooth has been growing in this man's head ninety-nine
> years before his great grandmother was born! If it
> hadn't been taken out today, he would have died
> yesterday.

He hands Jack the pincers, puts the tooth in his vest pocket,
and then points at the bottle Mother Dolly is holding, the pre-
cious bottle he had given her earlier, which she has protected
through thick and thin, through heave and haul, through tug
and tumble. She holds it high for all to see.

DOCTOR

> You see here a bottle of Hokum-Pokum!
> This little bottle never fails;
> With it I cure whatever ails.
> If this dead man will take one drop out of my bottle
> here, well shaken before taking *(he proceeds to act on
> his own instructions and shakes George vigorously),*
> he's sure to rise and fight no more!

The Doctor takes the bottle from Mother Dolly. He pours
a huge spoonful and administers it to Saint George, who chokes,
splutters, gasps, coughs, but finally comes to; he sits up, shakes
his head to clear it, and jumps to his feet! The children cheer.

SAINT GEORGE

> Good morning, gentles all.
> A-sleeping I have been,
> And such a sleep I've had,
> The like was never seen —
> I was knocked out of my seven senses
> Into seventeen!
> *(To the Turk)* But now I'm awake, the fight I'll resume,
> And quickly send thee to thy doom!

George lifts his sword; the Turkish Knight backs away from him; George follows, and brings the sword down with a great whoosh! The tip of it slits the Turkish Knight's front. Out tumbles a long string of sausages, as the Turk crumples and sinks to the floor in his death throes.

LITTLE JOHNNY JACK

    (*Chants*) This poor old man is dead and gone,
    We never shall see him more.

He used to wear his Turkish coat
All buttoned down before.
FATHER CHRISTMAS
But now his Turkish coat is split,
And here upon the floor,
This poor old Turkish Knight is lying
In his purple gore.

DOCTOR

Ashes to ashes, dust to dust.

If God won't have you, the Devil must.

FATHER CHRISTMAS

Come in, Beelzebub!

In romps the Devil himself! What an ugly ragged black creature he is, from the curly black wig that tops his black mask to the toes of his muddy black boots. His smock is all rents and holes, except where it is patches. Around his humped shoulders is draped a cow's hide, with a brass bell dinging at its tail. In one hand he holds a long-handled skillet, in the other a wicked-looking club.

BEELZEBUB

> Here come I, old Beelzebub;
> On my shoulder I carry my club;
> In my hand a frying pan.
> Don't you think I'm a jolly old man?

FATHER CHRISTMAS

> Why have you been so long a-coming?

BEELZEBUB

> Well, I was coming up a long short straight crooked lane, and I met a bark and he dogged at me. So I went to a stick and cut a bush and gave him a rump on the thump. Then I went along a-standing still through a land where the houses were thatched with pancakes until I came to a big little low broad tall narrow house. I went up and knocked at the old woman and a door came out. She asked if I would eat a cup of cider and drink a bit of bread and cheese, and I said "No thanks, yes if you please." Then I picked up my frying pan and went my way, and here I am.

Beelzebub approaches the Turkish Knight and capers around him in glee.

> But soon I'll be a-turning the spit
> Over a fire that's long been lighted,
> Waiting in my deep black pit
> For this Turkish soldier, so benighted.
>> Up, Turkish sire —
>> Time for the fire!

The Turkish Knight jumps to his feet and tries to escape his fell fate. Round and round he runs with the Devil after him, brandishing club and frying pan, and off into the dark outer regions of the entryway. No sooner have they disappeared than there somersaults in one of the strangest characters imaginable.

Wisps of straw are escaping from his huge stuffed head, which is covered all over with orange yarn hair. His shirt is a gay patchwork affair similar to Johnny Jack's, and bells jingle merrily on garters at his knees. "Big Head!" shriek the children. "It's Big Head!" And surely it can be no one else.

BIG HEAD

> Here come I, as ain't been yit,
> With my big head and little wit.
> My head is big, my wit is small,
> But I'll sing a song to please you all.

FATHER CHRISTMAS

What song can you sing?

BIG HEAD

Let me study a minute. *(His wrinkled brow shows that he is thinking hard.)* Oh! I've studied a love song about murder! My grandmother learned it me seven years after she was dead.

MOTHER DOLLY

I like a love song.

Big Head throws back his head, opens his mouth and sings lustily to the tune of "Good King Wenceslaus."

BIG HEAD

Love it is a killing thing
Both for heart and mind,
And he that doesn't come before
Needs must come before.
Oh, Love it is —

FATHER CHRISTMAS

Wait! Hold on, you old fool. What difference is

there between before and before? Sing it over again, and sing it right.

But Big Head crosses his arms on his chest and shakes his head stubbornly.

BIG HEAD

    No. I'll not sing it again.

SAINT GEORGE

    Sing it over again, and sing it right, or off goes your head!

With that Saint George brandishes his trusty sword.

BIG HEAD

    Oh, I'll sing it again. (*And he does.*)
    Love it is a killing thing,

Both for heart and mind,
And he that doesn't come before
Needs must come before.

FATHER CHRISTMAS

You did it again, you old fool! What difference is
there between before and before?

BIG HEAD

(Pouting) It's the way I learned it. Sing it yourself.

FATHER CHRISTMAS

If I sing it, see that you learn it. *(And Father
Christmas sings.)*
Love it is a killing thing,
Both for heart and mind,
And he that doesn't come before
Needs must come beHIND!
Now sing!

So, with Saint George's sword hanging heavy over him, Big
Head joins in on the chorus (same words, different music) —
and gets it right.

FATHER CHRISTMAS AND BIG HEAD
>   Love it is a killing thing
>   Both for heart and mind,
>   And he that doesn't come before
>   Needs must come behind!

FATHER CHRISTMAS
Now, let the music play, and make the sleigh bells ring!
A sip of Christmas punch will make us laugh and sing —
But money in our pocket is a much better thing!

BEELZEBUB

    (Returning) If this old frying pan had but a tongue,

    He'd say "chuck in your money and think it no wrong."

From Father Christmas's pack one of the mummers produces a recorder and plays a gay tune. With their sleigh bells jingling merrily, the other mummers collect pennies in hats and pans. Even the Turkish Knight returns to pass his turban — but he is careful to keep a safe distance away from Beelzebub.

FATHER CHRISTMAS

We thank you for your pennies, and your sixpences too;

We hope that on this Christmas time we've brought good cheer to you.

Now since our play is ended; we'll stay no longer here,

But wish you merry Christmas and a happy New Year!

Be there fire on your hearth, good luck for your lot —

Money in your pocket, and a pudding in your pot!

Then, singing a Christmas carol, the mummers retreat to the entrance hall, there to gather their paraphernalia and be off into the night. But they are not to escape without a struggle. Behind them crowd the children, the littlest gazing in awe at these marvelous creatures, the big ones begging the mummers to stay a while, for they are not content to have this part of their Christmas over and done so soon.

Someone places a bench for the mummers in the cleared space where the stage had been, and there they seat themselves. And there they are fed and wassailed and subjected to a heady mixture of adoration and adulation by the excited children.

Grown-ups go back to their conversations, having taken the mummers' performance matter-of-factly, as the routine bit of Christmas cheer that it is, one they have observed dozens of times. But no matter how old the custom, the children are always new. For some of them this is their first taste of real Drama, and all of them want to savor every crumb of it. They exclaim over the Dragon's long jagged green tail, and the cardboard wings that droop from his shoulders. They put on Saint George's high conical helmet and peep out between the strips of ribbon that hang from the front of it as a visor. They pat the Hobby Horse's nose, and touch the Devil's horns. One of them even musters up courage to sit on Father Christmas's knee.

So it goes until bedtime, and then it is over. The mummers depart into the snowy darkness from which they came.

But visions of Saint George will stride through the dreams of the sleeping children for many nights, and nurseries will echo the Dragon's roars for many days. The magic must last them a whole, long year.

And it will.

NOTES

Mumming is a Christmas tradition with which most of today's children are unfamiliar, but it can contribute too much to the fun and frivolity of the holiday season to be allowed to disappear forever into the past. Therefore, it is hoped that the following suggestions will enable many children to make it a part of Christmas present.

A mummers' play can be enjoyed within the home as part of family fun, costumed with odds and ends, or it can adapt itself to formal presentation on a stage, with as elaborate a production as ingenuity can devise. A welcome can even be engendered for roving mummers where no such tradition exists, if a group who want to produce the play distribute to friends and neighbors announcements of their availability as entertainers for holiday parties.

Fortunately, whatever the circumstances, the production is fraught with few problems. Nothing is needed by way of scenery, only a bare playing space, which can be on a stage or in the center of a schoolroom or living room. Nothing is needed by way of lighting effects. The few properties can all be carried by the actors who use them, or in Father Christmas's bag (a bag which, incidentally, is not traditional to the Father Christmas of mummers' plays). The simple sound effects can be provided by an offstage member of the cast.

The action itself is of the simplest. The characters enter, stand together in a stiff line or knot until time to make their speeches. Then they fight; they fall; they get up and go out. Even the Doctor usually did nothing more than make speeches and administer his medicine. In the present case we have borrowed from a Gloucestershire version that put considerably more action (and more fun) into the Doctor's ministrations. Otherwise little ensemble playing is required. Each actor takes the stage when his turn comes and puts into his part as much histrionic bluff and bluster as he likes, limited only by the size of the playing space available. In one known version the Dragon apparently engaged in some acrobatics, because his speeches at several points include lines like "Stand on head, stand on feet." Many mummers' plays also incorporated sword dancing or morris dancing. Therefore, folk dancing in conjunction with the play would be completely appropriate.

If desirable, the final collection (or *"quête"* as it is usually called) can easily be omitted. Simply omit the two speeches that follow the end of Big Head's song, and jump to the last four lines of Father Christmas's final speech. It is as simple as that.

If there is need to expand the cast, the Hobby Horse and the Doctor can be played by different actors. In that case there need to be several slight modifications. The doctor will enter and take the horse's bridle after Mother Dolly's "Is there a Doctor to be found to cure this deep and deadly wound?" The horse whinnies and the Doctor says "Whoa, boy, whoa." Then on with the play — except that the Doctor can no longer use the Hobby Horse as a weapon against Johnny Jack; but he has his wooden spoon. The horse can remain on the stage throughout the play and join in the fun. He can be produced as the "strongest hoss on the team" to help out in the tooth pulling, and that episode can even be stretched out almost *ad infinitum* by having the Doctor go on to ask for the next strongest horse, and so on.

If, on the other hand, a smaller cast is desired, it would be a simple matter to double some of the parts, or even eliminate someone like Big Head. The Dragon and Beelzebub would make a fine pair for doubling. Also, Mother Dolly might slip quietly away after giving the Doctor his bottle of Hokum-Pokum (she never speaks again), and return later as Big Head.

Nothing remains to be considered now but the costuming.

Thoughts about costumes turn first to how the plays may have been costumed originally. But descriptions of how the mummers looked are very scarce, and none are earlier than the nineteenth century, by which time many traditions had probably come and gone. Therefore, in the following discussion we shall make only a gesture in the direction of tradition and then go on to create costumes that today's children may find appropriate.

An 1848 source describes the mummers as being in white, with ribbons tied on their shirt sleeves, and with napkins and swords and such caps as had never been seen: "half a fathom high made of pastyboord, weth powers of beads and loaking glass, and other noshions, and strids of ould cloth . . . hanging down." [1] Except for the hat, the description very nearly fits the costumes worn by present-day morris dancers, and that is as good a model as any to keep in mind: white shirts, knee pants and socks, with belled garters at knees and gay colored ribbons tied around sleeves. The high hats mentioned here are described in other sources as "conical," "pointed," "foolscaps," and "mitres," and hats meeting some such description would be appropriate for the knights as approximations to high, pointed medieval

helmets (the "strids of cloth" hanging down were to simulate visors). A fool's cap might also be appropriate for Johnny Jack or Big Head. But for the other characters something else will have to be devised.

The white dress of the mummers was nothing more than the farm boys' smock-like shirts, long, full, and usually collarless, with appropriate (and sometimes inappropriate) decorations. In *The Return of the Native* (Book II, chapter 4) Thomas Hardy has this to say of costuming:

> Without the cooperation of sisters and sweethearts the dresses were likely to be a failure; but on the other hand, this class of assistance was not without its drawbacks. The girls could never be brought to respect tradition in designing and decorating the armour [what was that earlier "tradition"? we wonder]; they insisted on attaching loops and bows of silk and velvet in any situation pleasing to their taste. . . .

> It might be that Joe, who fought on the side of Christendom, had a sweetheart, and that Jim, who fought on the side of the Moslem, had one likewise. During the making of the

costumes it could come to the knowledge of Joe's sweetheart that Jim's was putting brilliant silk scallops at the bottom of her lover's surcoat. . . . Joe's sweetheart straightway placed brilliant silk on the scallops of the hem in question, and going a little further, added ribbon tufts to the shoulder pieces. Jim's, not to be outdone, would affix bows and rosettes everywhere.

The result was that in the end . . . Saint George might be mistaken for his deadly enemy, the Saracen. The guisers themselves, though inwardly regretting this confusion of persons, could not afford to offend those by whose assistance they so largely profited, and the innovations were allowed to stand.

Another fairly general tradition was for the characters to wear masks or to blacken or redden their faces — for mummers were also called "guisers" ("disguisers," that is). Today, however, masks can be done away with, except for Beelzebub and the Dragon.

But, to get back to our immediate problem: a good basic costume might consist of ordinary trousers in appropriate colors (e.g., light for Saint George, dark for the Turkish Knight) and long-sleeved shift-like tunics — sleeveless tunics over long-sleeved jerseys would do just as well. With this in mind, let us now begin at the beginning and discuss each character in turn.

LITTLE JOHNNY JACK was usually dressed in what has for centuries been traditional for clowns: multicolored patchwork. To this day May Day morris dancers in England are accompanied by a comic in a patched jacket who bounces around waving an inflated bladder on the end of a stick. Even Harlequin's famous diamond checks are in the same tradition; the patchwork is simply formalized. Therefore, for Johnny Jack a patched tunic and a balloon on a short stick. Somewhere he should also have bells to jingle, either on his costume or, preferably, on the stick of his balloon. Some kind of hat or wig, or even a jester's coxcomb, would complete his costume.

FATHER CHRISTMAS. The traditional figure of Father Christmas was said to be an older man in a white wig, who carried a gigantic club. The club is a convention that would be completely puzzling today. On the other hand the jolly fat man in the red suit would be equally out of place, since he was invented only fairly recently. Therefore, to resolve this dilemma, perhaps Father Christmas could be dressed in a costume that is neither one nor the other. White hair and beard seem appropriate in any case, and a crown of holly would not be out of place (such a wreath encircles the head of Dickens's Ghost of Christmas Present, for example). Complete the costume with neutral-colored trousers and a tunic of red or green bordered with white fur (Dickens chose green), and we have a Father Christmas that ought to be acceptable to almost anyone.

Hobby Horse. In actual fact the Hobby Horse is more usually associated with May Day celebrations than with Christmas mummers' plays. But he is a delightful character, so here he is. A child's stick hobbyhorse is the basis for his costume. The boy playing the horse holds the stick and is hidden by a full skirt falling from the horse's head down to his knees. A yarn tail for the back of the skirt adds a nice touch.

Mother Dolly. The most important item is a long full skirt, of almost any kind and color, worn over long-sleeved jersey and trousers. To enable her to play her dual role she needs a wig, and a kerchief to cover it. Give her a broom and her outfit is complete.

Saint George wears a white sleeveless tunic emblazoned with a large red cross, over white, or light-colored, trousers and jersey. A peaked helmet made of posterboard faced with silver paper and perhaps encircled by a gold crown is on his head; a wooden sword hangs at his side.

TURKISH KNIGHT. A black tunic, decorated with green or yellow crescent and star, over black trousers and jersey make a good contrast with Saint George. On the other hand, there is no real reason why he should not be colorful and wear a yellow or green tunic with black insignia. A peaked helmet, or turban, might also bear the crescent and star. His tunic must close down the front with snap fasteners, so that a sharp jerk will open it and allow coiled rope or strings of rubber frankfurters to fall out. A curved golden scimitar would make a handsome sword for him.

FIERY DRAGON. Now here is a problem that seems to have taxed the skills and resources of village sisters and sweethearts — because, surprising as it may be, the Dragon only rarely made an appearance in mummers' plays. E. K. Chambers guesses that his absence may have been due primarily to the difficulty of costuming him. But let us hope the difficulty will not be found insurmountable. Begin with dark trousers and matching jersey, blue or green, or even black. Over this put a sleeveless green tailcoat — one with an extravagantly long tail with a long spiney fin sewed into the center back

seam. Cover his head with a hood that comes well down over the
eyes and fastens snugly under the chin (with eye-holes, of course).
A snug hood gives a firm base to which to attach cardboard jaws,
and the more snugly the hood fits, the less the jaws are likely to sag.
Add wings, as simple or elegant as you wish to make them, and behold:
a Dragon!

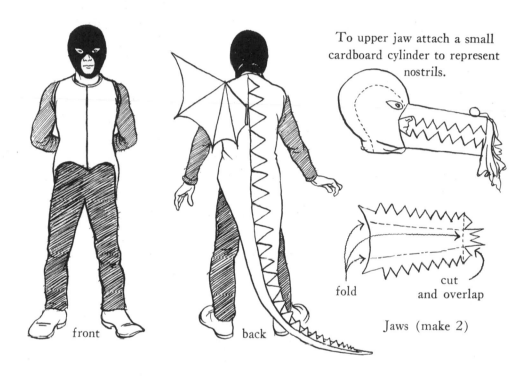

To upper jaw attach a small
cardboard cylinder to represent
nostrils.

fold

cut
and overlap

Jaws (make 2)

front

back

THE DOCTOR traditionally wore black: trousers, tailcoat, and
top hat (or three-cornered "piked" hat). A colorful cravat would
keep him from being too somber. He also wore spectacles and carried
a black bag. Hat and bag are difficult to manage if one is doubling
as the Hobby Horse; therefore they can be left off, and the Doctor's
implements can be carried in Father Christmas's bag. If, on the other
hand, Horse and Doctor are played by different actors, the Doctor
could appear in full regalia, and Father Christmas would then not
need to carry a bag.

BEELZEBUB always wore a mask or had his face blackened, so the
first requirement is a fearful-looking black mask, preferably one with
horns. In addition, his costume usually included one or all of the
following: a tail, a hump, a curly black wig, and a bell. He may also
have been the character who wore "a strange garb resembling sheep-
skins" that was mentioned in one source.[2] Therefore, an appropriate

costume might consist of black trousers and a ragged black tunic over a humped back. If he has a calfskin to drape around his shoulders, so much the better. Hanging from the back of tunic or calfskin there could be a tail and a small cowbell. He carries a club and frying pan, as he says.

BIG HEAD. As his name implies Big Head has a big head as his most prominent identifying feature. Make an oversized hood, stuff it with rags, and cover it with orange yarn stitched through it loosely at one-inch intervals in rows an inch apart. Aside from his head, any traditional difference between Big Head and Johnny Jack is difficult to find. He, also, can wear a patched tunic. In addition he might borrow an idea from the morris dancers and tuck his trousers into knee socks held up by jingle-bell garters. As a final touch he might redden his face.

And there's an end. Our mummers' play is ready — this link with the long ago, this echo from Christmas past.

[1] Quoted by E. K. Chambers in *The English Folk-Play* (Oxford: Clarendon Press, 1933), p. 83.
[2] Quoted by Chambers, *op. cit.,* p. 84.

Sources:

1. Chambers, E. K., *The English Folk-Play*. Oxford, Clarendon Press, 1933.
2. Hardy, Thomas, *The Play of St. George,* as reconstructed from memory. New York: Samuel French, 1928.
3. Long, George, *The Folklore Calendar*. London: Philip Allan, 1930.
4. Manly, John Matthews, *Specimens of the Pre-Shaksperean Drama.* Vol. I. Boston and London, Ginn & Co., The Athenaeum Press, 1900.
5. Sharp, Cecil J., *The Sword Dances of Northern England,* Part III. London: Novello & Co., Ltd., 1913.
6. Tiddy, Reginald John Elliott, *The Mummers' Play*. Oxford, Clarendon Press, 1923.